Dazzling DIGGERS

ISBN 0-439-22916-2

Text copyright © 1997 by Tony Mitton.
Illustrations copyright © 1997 by Ant Parker. All rights reserved.
Published by Scholastic Inc., 555 Broadway, New York, NY 10012,
by arrangement with Larousse Kingfisher Chambers Inc. SCHOLASTIC and
associated logos are trademarks and/or registered trademarks of Scholastic Inc.

12 11 10 9 8 7 6 5 4 3 2 1   1 2 3 4 5 6/0

Printed in the U.S.A.   23

First Scholastic printing, February 2001

Dazzling DIGGERS

Tony Mitton and Ant Parker

SCHOLASTIC INC.

New York Toronto London Auckland Sydney
Mexico City New Delhi Hong Kong

Diggers are noisy, strong, and big.

Diggers can carry and push and dig.

Diggers have shovels to scoop and lift,

Scrunch

blades that bulldoze, shunt, and shift.

Diggers have buckets to gouge out ground,

breakers that crack and smash and pound.

Diggers move rubble and rocks and soil,

so diggers need drinks of diesel oil.

Some have tires and some have tracks.

Some keep steady with legs called jacks.

Tires and tracks grip hard as they travel,

squish through mud and grind through gravel.

Diggers go scrunch and squelch and slosh.

This dirty digger needs a really good wash.

Diggers can bash and crash and break,

make things crumble, shiver, and shake.

Diggers can heave and hoist and haul.

Diggers help buildings tower up tall.

Drivers park neatly, down on the site.

And then they all go home. Goodnight!

Digger parts

levers

these control different parts of the digger

tire

this helps the wheel to grip the ground and get the digger moving

bucket

this is for digging and scooping out

jack

this holds the digger steady when it is lifting or digging

piston

this is a strong pump that makes parts of the digger move around

breaker

this is for cracking concrete or lumps of rock

tracks

these help the digger to travel over slippery or bumpy ground

blade

this is for knocking down and pushing along